S0-AVC-892

KNOCK KNOCK KNOCK JOKES

KNOCK KNOCK JOKES

Door-knocking, knee-slapping, rib-tickling fun!

ARCTURUS

ARCTURUS
This edition published in 2010 by Arcturus Publishing Limited
26/27 Bickels Yard, 151–153 Bermondsey Street,
London SE1 3HA

Copyright © 2010 Arcturus Publishing Limited

All rights reserved. No part of this publication may be reproduced,
stored in a retrieval system, or transmitted, in any form or by any
means, electronic, mechanical, photocopying, recording or otherwise,
without written permission in accordance with the provisions of the
Copyright Act 1956 (as amended). Any person or persons who do
any unauthorised act in relation to this publication may be liable to
criminal prosecution and civil claims for damages.

ISBN: 978-1-84837-632-8
CH001576EN

Design and Editorial: Moseley Strachan
Illustrations: Quadrum

Printed in India

KNOCK, KNOCK...

Knock, knock...
Who's there?
Butter...
Butter who?
Butter bring an umbrella,
it looks like it might rain!

Knock, knock...
Who's there?
Dino...
Dino who?
Dino the answer!

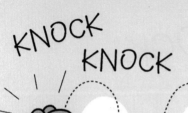

KNOCK KNOCK

Knock, knock...
Who's there?
Chimney...
Chimney who?
Chimney cricket!
Have you seen Pinocchio?

Knock, knock...
Who's there?
Ya...
Ya who?
What are you getting so
excited about?

Knock, knock...
Who's there?
Wood...
Wood who?
Wood you like to let me in now?

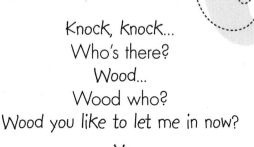

Knock, knock...
Who's there?
Theodore...
Theodore who?
Theodore is stuck and it won't open!

Knock, knock...
Who's there?
Larva...
Larva who?
Larva cup of coffee.

7

KNOCK KNOCK

Knock, knock...
Who's there?
Lettuce...
Lettuce who?
Lettuce in and you will find out!

Knock, knock...
Who's there?
Dot...
Dot who?
Dots for me to know, and you
to find out.

Knock, knock...
Who's there?
Toby...
Toby who?
Toby or not to be!

Knock, knock...
Who's there?
Carter...
Carter who?
Carter stray dog - is it yours?

Knock, knock...
Who's there?
Cargo...
Cargo who?
Cargo beep! beep!

KNOCK KNOCK

Knock, knock...
Who's there?
Icon...
Icon who?
Icon tell you another knock, knock joke
if you want me to!

Knock, knock...
Who's there?
Avon...
Avon who?
Avon to trink your blood!

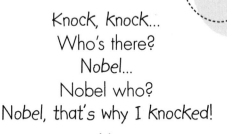

Knock, knock...
Who's there?
Nobel...
Nobel who?
Nobel, that's why I knocked!

Knock, knock...
Who's there?
Ben...
Ben who?
Ben wondering what you're up to!

Knock, knock...
Who's there?
Andrew...
Andrew who?
Andrew all over the wall!

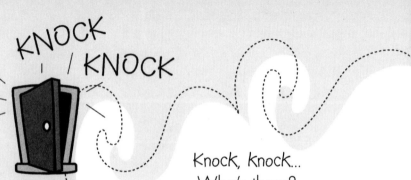

KNOCK KNOCK

Knock, knock...
Who's there?
Castor...
Castor who?
Castorblanca!

Knock, knock...
Who's there?
Ferdie...
Ferdie who?
Ferdie last time, open this door!

Knock, knock...
Who's there?
Fonda...
Fonda who?
Fonda you!

Knock, knock...
Who's there?
Philip...
Philip who?
Philip my glass will you please!

Knock, knock...
Who's there?
Jester...
Jester who?
Jester minute, I'm trying to find my keys!

KNOCK KNOCK

Knock, knock...
Who's there?
Henrietta...
Henrietta who?
Henrietta toadstool but thought
it was a mushroom!

Knock, knock...
Who's there?
Ford...
Ford who?
Ford he's a jolly good fellow!

Knock, knock...
Who's there?
Hans...
Hans who?
Hans off the table!

Knock, knock...
Who's there?
Harlow...
Harlow who?
Harlow will you go!

Knock, knock...
Who's there?
Butternut...
Butternut who?
Butternut squash the eggs!

KNOCK
/ KNOCK

Knock, knock...
Who's there?
Wendy...
Wendy who?
Wendy wind *blows de* cradle will rock.

Knock, knock...
Who's there?
Butter...
Butter who?
Butter let me in!

Knock, knock...
Who's there?
A little girl...
A little girl who?
A little girl who can't reach the
doorbell!

Knock, knock...
Who's there?
Louis...
Louis who?
Louis'n up!

Knock, knock...
Who's there?
Adolf...
Adolf who?
Adolf ball hit me in de mouf!

KNOCK KNOCK

Knock, knock...
Who's there?
Kent...
Kent who?
Kent you stop asking questions
and open the door!

Knock, knock...
Who's there?
Sacha...
Sacha who?
Sacha fuss, just because
I knocked on your door!

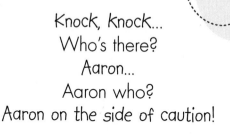

Knock, knock...
Who's there?
Aaron...
Aaron who?
Aaron on the side of caution!

Knock, knock...
Who's there?
Orange...
Orange who?
Orange you glad I didn't say banana?

Knock, knock...
Who's there?
Heidi...
Heidi who?
Heidi-clare war on you!

KNOCK / KNOCK

Knock, knock...
Who's there?
Kline...
Kline who?
Kline of you to invite me round!

Knock, knock...
Who's there?
Water...
Water who?
Water you doing in my house?

Knock, knock...
Who's there?
Wendy...
Wendy who?
Wendy you want me to
call round again?

Knock, knock...
Who's there?
Lisbon...
Lisbon who?
Lisbon married six times!

Knock, knock...
Who's there?
Courtney...
Courtney who?
Courtney door, can you open
it and let me loose?

KNOCK KNOCK

Knock, knock...
Who's there?
Sid...
Sid who?
Sid you'd be ready by three –
where are you?!

Knock, knock...
Who's there?
Mary...
Mary who?
Mary Christmas, ho, ho, ho!

Knock, knock...
Who's there?
Beethoven...
Beethoven who?
Beethoven is too hot!

Knock, knock...
Who's there?
Dill...
Dill who?
Dill we meet again!

☼

Knock, knock...
Who's there?
Deduct...
Deduct who?
Donald Deduct!

23

KNOCK / KNOCK

Knock, knock...
Who's there?
Safari...
Safari who?
Safari *so* good...

Knock, knock...
Who's there?
Carla...
Carla who?
Carla taxi, I'm leaving!

Knock, knock...
Who's there?
Sally...
Sally who?
Sally-brate the *best* moments
of your life!

Knock, knock...
Who's there?
Violet...
Violet who?
Violet the cat out of the bag!

Knock, knock...
Who's there?
Farmer...
Farmer who?
Farmer distance your house
looks much bigger!

KNOCK
KNOCK

Knock, knock...
Who's there?
Luke...
Luke who?
Luke through the keyhole
and you'll see...

※

Knock, knock...
Who's there?
Ringo...
Ringo who?
Ringo, ringo roses...!

Knock, knock...
Who's there?
Morgan...
Morgan who?
Morgan you could ever imagine!

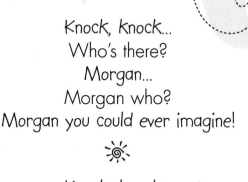

Knock, knock...
Who's there?
Hardy...
Hardy who?
Hardy har, fooled you!

Knock, knock...
Who's there?
Teresa...
Teresa who?
Teresa jolly good fellow!

KNOCK / KNOCK

Knock, knock...
Who's there?
Courtney...
Courtney who?
Courtney good football matches lately?

Knock, knock...
Who's there?
Tessa...
Tessa who?
Tessa long time for you
to open the door!

Knock, knock...
Who's there?
Ray...
Ray who?
Ray-ders of the Lost Ark!

28

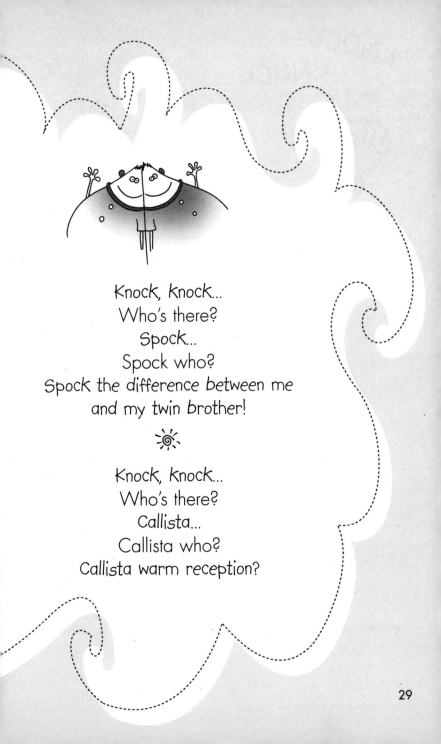

Knock, knock...
Who's there?
Spock...
Spock who?
Spock the difference between me
and my twin brother!

Knock, knock...
Who's there?
Callista...
Callista who?
Callista warm reception?

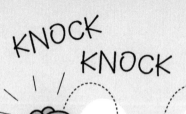

KNOCK KNOCK

Knock, knock...
Who's there?
Batman...
Batman who?
You mean there's
more than one?!

Knock, knock...
Who's there?
Wendy...
Wendy who?
Wendy red, red robin comes bob,
bob bobbin' along, along...

Knock, knock...
Who's there?
Seymour...
Seymour who?
Seymour of me by opening the door!

Knock, knock...
Who's there?
Sid...
Sid who?
Sid down and I'll explain!

Knock, knock...
Who's there?
Usher...
Usher who?
Usher wish you would let me in!

KNOCK KNOCK

Knock, knock...
Who's there?
Chris...
Chris who?
Chris packets make a lot of
noise in the cinema!

Knock, knock...
Who's there?
Icing...
Icing who?
Icing carols - you give me money!

Knock, knock...
Who's there?
Jethro...
Jethro who?
Jethro this at me?

Knock, knock...
Who's there?
Jaffa...
Jaffa who?
Jaffa keep me waiting?

Knock, knock...
Who's there?
Just Paul...
Just Paul who?
Just Pauling your leg - it's Steve really!

KNOCK KNOCK

Knock, knock...
Who's there?
Walter...
Walter who?
Walter strange thing to ask!

Knock, knock...
Who's there?
Posh...
Posh who?
Posh the door open and you'll see!

Knock, knock...
Who's there?
Wade...
Wade who?
Wade a minute, I'll just check!

☀

Knock, knock...
Who's there?
Vince...
Vince who?
Vince some time since I saw you last!

☀

Knock, knock...
Who's there?
Jerome...
Jerome who?
Jerome at last!

Knock, knock...
Who's there?
May...
May who?
May I come in?

Knock, knock...
Who's there?
Will...
Will who?
Will wait out here until you let us in!

Knock, knock...
Who's there?
Terminator...
Terminator who?
Terminator sandwiches early,
so she sent me to get some more!

Knock, knock...
Who's there?
Norbut...
Norbut who?
Norbut a lad!

☀

Knock, knock...
Who's there?
Baby...
Baby who?
Baby I shouldn't hab come
round wiv dis cold!

KNOCK KNOCK

Knock, knock...
Who's there?
Russell...
Russell who?
Russell up a nice hot cup of tea -
it's freezing out here!

Knock, knock...
Who's there?
Belle...
Belle who?
Belle don't work,
so I'm having to knock!

Knock, knock...
Who's there?
You...
You who?
Hello!

☀

Knock, knock...
Who's there?
Otto...
Otto who?
Ottold you not two seconds ago!

☀

Knock, knock...
Who's there?
Lucinda...
Lucinda who?
Lucinda sky with diamonds...

Knock, knock...
Who's there?
Misty...
Misty who?
Misty door bell again!

Knock, knock...
Who's there?
Olive...
Olive who?
Olive none of your lip!

Knock, knock...
Who's there?
Fitz...
Fitz who?
Fitz not too much trouble,
can you please open the door?!

Knock, knock...
Who's there?
Posy...
Posy who?
Posy open the door and find out?

Knock, knock...
Who's there?
Lass...
Lass who?
How long have you been a cowboy?

KNOCK KNOCK

Knock, knock...
Who's there?
Ozzie...
Ozzie who?
Ozzie you still have the same
front door you did the last time I called!

Knock, knock...
Who's there?
Doctor...
Doctor who?
No, Doctor Smith - you sent for me
because you have a cold!

Knock, knock...
Who's there?
Mayor...
Mayor who?
Mayor come in?

Knock, knock...
Who's there?
Willy...
Willy who?
Willy hurry up and let me in!

Knock, knock...
Who's there?
Lester...
Lester who?
Lester worry about!

KNOCK KNOCK

Knock, knock...
Who's there?
Homer...
Homer who?
Homer goodness - I can't remember
myself!

Knock, knock...
Who's there?
Bart...
Bart who?
Bart time you opened this door!

Knock, knock...
Who's there?
Fred...
Fred who?
Fred you'll have to
let me in!

Knock, knock...
Who's there?
Giselle...
Giselle who?
Giselle flowers in there?

Knock, knock...
Who's there?
Mustapha...
Mustapha who?
Mustapha good reason to keep
me waiting!

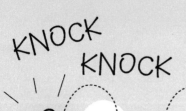

KNOCK KNOCK

Knock, knock...
Who's there?
Karl...
Karl who?
I'll Karl round again another day
when you're feeling better!

Knock, knock...
Who's there?
Jester...
Jester who?
Jester day, all my troubles
seemed so far away...!

Knock, knock...
Who's there?
Butcher...
Butcher who?
Butcher said I could come and visit you!

Knock, knock...
Who's there?
Lefty...
Lefty who?
Lefty home on your own again!

Knock, knock...
Who's there?
Dan...
Dan who?
Dan just stand there - let me in!

KNOCK KNOCK

Knock, knock...
Who's there?
Arthur...
Arthur who?
Arthur minute and I'll show
you my identification!

Knock, knock...
Who's there?
Wallace...
Wallace who?
Wallace is a fine how do you do...!

Knock, knock...
Who's there?
Joanna...
Joanna who?
Joanna have a guess?

Knock, knock...
Who's there?
Wendy...
Wendy who?
Wendy come to collect the rent,
I'm off!

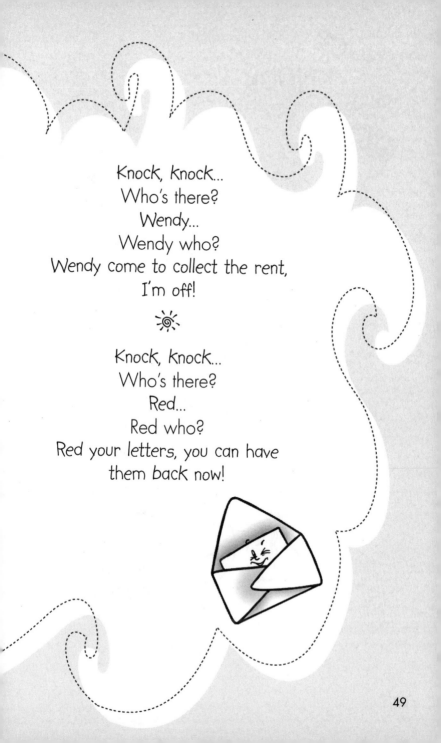

Knock, knock...
Who's there?
Red...
Red who?
Red your letters, you can have
them back now!

KNOCK KNOCK

Knock, knock...
Who's there?
Charlie...
Charlie who?
Charlie you know the sound
of my voice by now!

Knock, knock...
Who's there?
Pearce...
Pearce who?
Pearce this balloon with a pin!

Knock, knock...
Who's there?
Goat...
Goat who?
Goat to the door and find out!

Knock, knock...
Who's there?
Aware...
Aware who?
Aware, aware has my little dog gone?

Knock, knock...
Who's there?
Cello...
Cello who?
Cello dear!

KNOCK KNOCK

Knock, knock...
Who's there?
Elvis...
Elvis who?
Elvis is a complete waste of time, I'm off!

Knock, knock...
Who's there?
Aardvark...
Aardvark who?
Aardvark a million miles
for one of your smiles.

Knock, knock...
Who's there?
I love...
I love who?
I don't know, you tell me!

Knock, knock...
Who's there?
Howard...
Howard who?
Howard you know
if you won't even open the door?

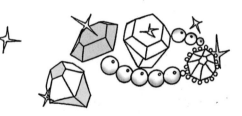

Knock, knock...
Who's there?
Jools...
Jools who?
Jools like these should be worth
a lot of money!

KNOCK KNOCK

Knock, knock...
Who's there?
Our Tell...
Our Tell who?
Our Tell you what I want,
what I really really want...!

Knock, knock...
Who's there?
Whoo ooo oooo ooo...
Whoo ooo oooo ooo who?
Ah, good, this is the ghost's club!

Knock, knock...
Who's there?
Doris...
Doris, who?
Doris locked, that's why I had to knock!

Knock, knock...
Who's there?
Goat...
Goat who?
Goat to the door and find out!

Knock, knock...
Who's there?
Boo...
Boo who?
Don't cry. It's only a joke!

KNOCK
KNOCK

Knock, knock...
Who's there?
Simon...
Simon who?
Simon every occasion -
you always make me wait!

Knock, knock...
Who's there?
Oliver...
Oliver who?
Oliver across the road from you!

Knock, knock...
Who's there?
Tank...
Tank who?
You're welcome!

Knock, knock...
Who's there?
Igloo...
Igloo who?
Igloo knew Suzie like I know Suzie...

Knock, knock...
Who's there?
Fletch...
Fletch who?
Fletch a bucket of water, your house
is on fire!

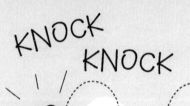

KNOCK KNOCK

Knock, knock...
Who's there?
Plato...
Plato who?
Plato fish and chips please!

Knock, knock...
Who's there?
Norma Lee...
Norma Lee who?
Norma Lee I don't go around knocking
on doors, but do you want to buy a
set of encyclopedias?

Knock, knock...
Who's there?
Jewell...
Jewell who?
Jewell know if you open the door!

Knock, knock...
Who's there?
Dime...
Dime who?
Dime to tell another knock, knock joke!

Knock, knock...
Who's there?
Despair...
Despair who?
Despair tyre is flat.

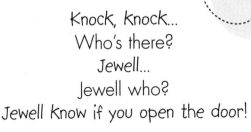

KNOCK / KNOCK

Knock, knock...
Who's there?
Closure...
Closure who?
Closure mouth when you're eating!

Knock, knock...
Who's there?
Argue...
Argue who?
Argue going to let me in or not???

Knock, knock...
Who's there?
Accordion...
Accordion who?
Accordion to the weather forecast,
it's going to rain tomorrow.

Knock, knock...
Who's there?
Howard...
Howard who?
Howard you like to be outside
for a change!

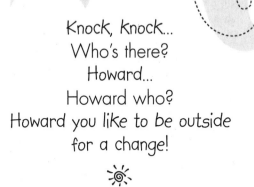

Knock, knock...
Who's there?
Olly...
Olly who?
Olly need is love!

KNOCK KNOCK

Knock, knock...
Who's there?
Buddha...
Buddha who?
Buddha this slice of bread for me.

Knock, knock...
Who's there?
Mickey...
Mickey who?
Mickey fell down the drain,
can you give me a lift?

Knock, knock...
Who's there?
Julia...
Julia who?
Julia want some milk and cookies?

Knock, knock...
Who's there?
Urchin...
Urchin who?
Urchin is pointy.

Knock, knock...
Who's there?
Havelock...
Havelock who?
Havelock put on your door!

Knock, knock...
Who's there?
Scott...
Scott who?
Scott nothing to do with you.

Knock, knock...
Who's there?
Kay...
Kay who?
Kay, L, M, N, O, P, Q, R, S, T, U,
V, W, X, Y, Z!

Knock, knock...
Who's there?
U-8...
U-8 who?
U-8 my lunch!

Knock, knock...
Who's there?
Honor Claire...
Honor Claire who?
Honor Claire day, you can *see* forever...!

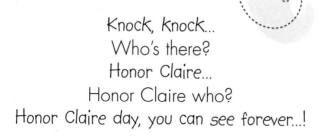

Knock, knock...
Who's there?
Wanda...
Wanda who?
Wanda know how much longer
you're going to keep me hanging
around out here!

KNOCK KNOCK

YO-OO-DLE-oo

Knock, knock...
Who's there?
Yodel...
Yodel who?
Yodel who to you too! Let's form
a yodelling duo!

Knock, knock...
Who's there?
C-2...
C-2 who?
C-2 it that you don't forget my name
next time!

Knock, knock...
Who's there?
Costas...
Costas who?
Costas a fortune to get here.

Knock, knock...
Who's there?
Hammond...
Hammond who?
Hammond eggs for breakfast.

Knock, knock...
Who's there?
Eyesore...
Eyesore who?
Eyesore do like you!

KNOCK KNOCK

Knock, knock...
Who's there?
Ike...
Ike who?
Ike can't stop laughing!

Knock, knock...
Who's there?
Lauren...
Lauren who?
Lauren order!

Knock, knock...
Who's there?
Cam...
Cam who?
Camelot is where
King Arthur lived.

Knock, knock...
Who's there?
Max...
Max who?
Max no difference.

Knock, knock...
Who's there?
Olive...
Olive who?
Olive you!

KNOCK KNOCK

Knock, knock...
Who's there?
Eileen...
Eileen who?
Eileen down to tie my shoe.

Knock, knock...
Who's there?
Hawaii...
Hawaii who?
I'm fine, Hawaii you?

Knock, knock...
Who's there?
Haden...
Haden who?
Haden *seek*.

Knock, knock...
Who's there?
Bacon...
Bacon who?
Bacon a cake for your birthday.

Knock, knock...
Who's there?
Zany...
Zany who?
Zany body home?

Knock, knock...
Who's there?
Eamonn...
Eamonn who?
Eamonn a good mood today, come in...

Knock, knock...
Who's there?
Dad...
Dad who?
Dad fuel to the fire!

Knock, knock...
Who's there?
Jacklyn...
Jacklyn who?
Jacklyn Hyde!

Knock, knock...
Who's there?
Candace...
Candace who?
Candace be true?

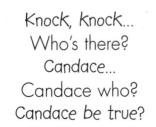

Knock, knock...
Who's there?
Who...
Who who?
Is there an owl in here?

KNOCK KNOCK

Knock, knock...
Who's there?
Anita...
Anita who?
Anita to borrow a pencil!

Knock, knock...
Who's there?
Element...
Element who?
Element to tell you that
she can't see you today.

Knock, knock...
Who's there?
May...
May who?
May the force be with you!

Knock, knock...
Who's there?
Queen...
Queen who?
Queen as a whistle!

Knock, knock...
Who's there?
Vampire...
Vampire who?
Vampire State Building!

KNOCK KNOCK

Knock, knock...
Who's there?
Mae...
Mae who?
Mae be I'll tell you or Mae be I won't...

Knock, knock...
Who's there?
Waddle...
Waddle who?
Waddle you give me if I go away?

Knock, knock...
Who's there?
Leaf...
Leaf who?
Leaf me alone!

Knock, knock...
Who's there?
Juicy...
Juicy who?
Juicy what I just saw?

Knock, knock...
Who's there?
Luck...
Luck who?
Luck through the key hole and
you'll find out.

KNOCK KNOCK

Knock, knock...
Who's there?
Lionel...
Lionel who?
Lionel bite you if you put
your head in its mouth!!!

Knock, knock...
Who's there?
Phyllis...
Phyllis who?
Phyllis up a cup of water!

Knock, knock...
Who's there?
Eye...
Eye who?
Eye know who you are!

Knock, knock...
Who's there?
Zizi...
Zizi who?
Zizi when you know how.

Knock, knock...
Who's there?
Bach...
Bach who?
Bach to work, you slackers!

KNOCK / KNOCK

Knock, knock...
Who's there?
Mabel...
Mabel who?
Mabel doesn't ring either...

Knock, knock...
Who's there?
Les...
Les who?
Les go for a swim!

Knock, knock...
Who's there?
Fanny...
Fanny who?
Fanny body calls, I'm out.

Knock, knock...
Who's there?
Archie...
Archie who?
Bless you!

Knock, knock...
Who's there?
Rather...
Rather who?
Rather not come in...

KNOCK KNOCK

Knock, knock...
Who's there?
Ear...
Ear who?
Ear you are! I've been looking for you!

Knock, knock...
Who's there?
Moo...
Moo, who?
Well, make up your mind,
are you a cow or an owl?

Knock, knock...
Who's there?
Zookeeper...
Zookeeper who?
Zookeeper away from him!

Knock, knock...
Who's there?
Abbott...
Abbott who?
Abbott time you opened this door!

Knock, knock...
Who's there?
Termite...
Termite who?
Termite's the night!

Knock, knock...
Who's there?
Waiter...
Waiter who?
Waiter minute while I tie my shoelaces.

Knock, knock...
Who's there?
Lisa...
Lisa who?
Lisa you can do is letta me in.

Knock, knock...
Who's there?
Madrid...
Madrid who?
Madrid you wash my jeans?

Knock, knock...
Who's there?
Cow-go...
Cow-go who?
No, Cow go MOO!!!

✺

Knock, knock...
Who's there?
Spell...
Spell who?
W...H...O!

KNOCK KNOCK

Knock, knock...
Who's there?
Cronkite...
Cronkite who?
Cronkite evidence!
Knock, knock...

Who's there?
I don't know...
I don't know who?
I told you I don't know.
Why don't you believe me?

Knock, knock...
Who's there?
Blue...
Blue who?
Blue away with the wind!

Knock, knock...
Who's there?
Imogen...
Imogen who?
Imogen life without chocolate!

Knock, knock...
Who's there?
Nuisance...
Nuisance who?
What's nuisance yesterday?

KNOCK KNOCK

Knock, knock...
Who's there?
Lionel...
Lionel who?
Lionel get you nowhere, better
tell the truth!

Knock, knock...
Who's there?
Ike...
Ike who?
Ike could have danced all night...

Knock, knock...
Who's there?
Bart...
Bart who?
Bart up the wrong tree!

88

Knock, knock...
Who's there?
Thaddeus...
Thaddeus who?
To be or not to be, Thaddeus
the question.

Knock, knock...
Who's there?
Ice cream...
Ice cream who?
Ice cream every time I see a ghost.

KNOCK KNOCK

Knock, knock...
Who's there?
Radio...
Radio who?
Radio not, here I come!

Knock, knock...
Who's there?
Norma Lee...
Norma Lee who?
Norma Lee I have my key.

Knock, knock...
Who's there?
Bargain...
Bargain who?
Bargain up the wrong tree!

Knock, knock...
Who's there?
Tara...
Tara who?
Tara-ra boom-de-ay!

Knock, knock...
Who's there?
Howie...
Howie who?
I'm fine, how are you!

KNOCK KNOCK

Knock, knock...
Who's there?
Vassar...
Vassar who?
Vassar girl like you doing in a place like this?

Knock, knock...
Who's there?
Borg...
Borg who?
Borg out of my mind!

Knock, knock...
Who's there?
Lenny...
Lenny who?
Lenny in, I'm hungry.

Knock, knock...
Who's there?
Nadia...
Nadia who?
Just Nadia head if you understand
what I'm saying.

☀

Knock, knock...
Who's there?
Omelette...
Omelette who?
Omelette smarter than I look!

KNOCK KNOCK

Knock, knock...
Who's there?
Gorilla...
Gorilla who?
Gorilla cheese sandwich for me
and I'll be right over.

Knock, knock...
Who's there?
Value...
Value who?
Value be my Valentine?

Knock, knock...
Who's there?
Sherwood...
Sherwood who?
Sherwood like to meet you!

Knock, knock...
Who's there?
Norway...
Norway who?
Norway will I leave till you open this door!

Knock, knock...
Who's there?
Theodore...
Theodore who?
Theodore wasn't open so I knocked!

KNOCK / KNOCK

Knock, knock...
Who's there?
Abyssinia...
Abyssinia who?
Abyssinia behind bars one of these days!

Knock, knock...
Who's there?
Boliva...
Boliva who?
Boliva me, I know what I'm talking about!

Knock, knock...
Who's there?
Sam...
Sam who?
Sam person who knocked
on the door last time!

Knock, knock...
Who's there?
Abbey...
Abbey who?
Abbey stung me on the nose!

Knock, knock...
Who's there?
Trixie...
Trixie who?
Trixie couldn't do because
he was a bad magician!

Knock, knock...
Who's there?
Thermos...
Thermos who?
Thermos be a better
knock, knock joke than this!

Knock, knock...
Who's there?
Ketchup...
Ketchup who?
Ketchup with me and I will tell you.

Knock, knock...
Who's there?
Albee...
Albee who?
Albee a monkey's uncle!

Knock, knock...
Who's there?
Alda...
Alda who?
Alda time you knew who it was!

Knock, knock...
Who's there?
Hand...
Hand who?
Hand over your wallet, this is a hold up!

KNOCK KNOCK

Knock, knock...
Who's there?
Ina...
Ina who?
Ina minute I'm going to knock
this door down!

Knock, knock...
Who's there?
Adelia...
Adelia who?
Adelia the cards and we'll play snap!

Knock, knock...
Who's there?
Ada...
Ada who?
Ada burger for lunch!

Knock, knock...
Who's there?
Veal chop...
Veal chop who?
Veal chop around and *see*
vot bargains vee can pick up!

Knock, knock...
Who's there?
Roach...
Roach who?
Roach out and touch someone.

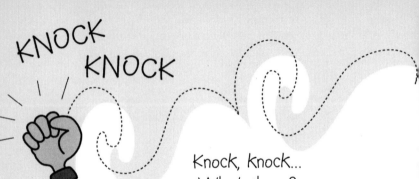

KNOCK KNOCK

Knock, knock...
Who's there?
Formosa...
Formosa who?
Formosa the summer I was away
on my holiday.

Knock, knock...
Who's there?
I-8...
I-8 who?
I-8 lunch already... Is dinner ready?

Knock, knock...
Who's there?
Alaska...
Alaska who?
Alaska my friend the question then!

Knock, knock...
Who's there?
Zippy...
Zippy who?
Zippy dee-doo-dah, zippy dee hey!

Knock, knock...
Who's there?
Beets...
Beets who?
Beets me!

KNOCK
KNOCK

Knock, knock...
Who's there?
Butter...
Butter who?
Butter open quick,
I have to go to the bathroom!

Knock, knock...
Who's there?
Arthur...
Arthur who?
Arthur any more biscuits in the tin?

Knock, knock...
Who's there?
Truffle...
Truffle who?
Truffle with you is that you are so shy.

Knock, knock...
Who's there?
Scold...
Scold who?
Scold outside.

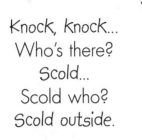

Knock, knock...
Who's there?
Reed...
Reed who?
Reed-turn to sender,
address unknown!

Knock, knock...
Who's there?
Rabbit...
Rabbit who?
Rabbit up carefully, it's a present!

Knock, knock...
Who's there?
Lucretia...
Lucretia who?
Lucretia from the Black Lagoon!

Knock, knock...
Who's there?
Reed...
Reed who?
Reed between the lines.

Knock, knock...
Who's there?
Anthem...
Anthem who?
You Anthem devil you!

Knock, knock...
Who's there?
Arbus...
Arbus who?
Arbus leaves in 5 minutes!

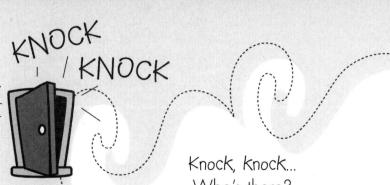

KNOCK KNOCK

Knock, knock...
Who's there?
Apple...
Apple who?
Apple your hair if
you don't let me in!

Knock, knock...
Who's there?
Anna...
Anna who?
Anna gonna tell you!

Knock, knock...
Who's there?
Anne Boleyn...
Anne Boleyn who?
Anne Boleyn alley!

Knock, knock...
Who's there?
Dexter...
Dexter who?
Dexter halls with boughs of holly.

Knock, knock...
Who's there?
Annetta...
Annetta who?
Annetta wisecrack and you're
out of here!

KNOCK KNOCK

Knock, knock...
Who's there?
Anita...
Anita who?
Anita you like I need a hole
in the head!

Knock, knock...
Who's there?
Uriah...
Uriah who?
Keep Uriah on the ball!

Knock, knock...
Who's there?
Amy...
Amy who?
Amy fraid I've forgotten!

Knock, knock...
Who's there?
Andrew...
Andrew who?
Andrew a picture!

Knock, knock...
Who's there?
Althea...
Althea who?
Althea later, alligator!

KNOCK KNOCK

Knock, knock...
Who's there?
Alpaca...
Alpaca who?
Alpaca the trunk, you packa the suitcase!

Knock, knock...
Who's there?
Allied...
Allied who?
Allied, so sue me!

Knock, knock...
Who's there?
Alfie...
Alfie who?
Alfie terrible if you leave!

Knock, knock...
Who's there?
Alva...
Alva who?
Alva heart!

Knock, knock...
Who's there?
Aida...
Aida who?
Aida lot of sweets and
now I've got tummy ache!

KNOCK KNOCK

Knock, knock...
Who's there?
Ollie...
Ollie who?
Ollie time you say that,
I wish you would cut it out!

Knock, knock...
Who's there?
Garden...
Garden who?
Garden the treasure.

Knock, knock...
Who's there?
Alexia...
Alexia who?
Alexia again to open this door!

Knock, knock...
Who's there?
Alfalfa...
Alfalfa who?
Alfalfa you, if you give me a kiss!

Knock, knock...
Who's there?
Ivor...
Ivor who?
Ivor good mind not to tell you now!

Knock, knock...
Who's there?
Atlas...
Atlas who?
Atlas it's the weekend!

Knock, knock...
Who's there?
Aunt Lou...
Aunt Lou who?
Aunt Lou do you think you are?

Knock, knock...
Who's there?
Axl...
Axl who?
Axl me nicely and I might
just tell you!

Knock, knock...
Who's there?
Tennis...
Tennis who?
Tennis five plus five.

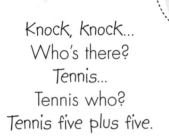

Knock, knock...
Who's there?
Beezer...
Beezer who?
Beezer black and yellow and
make honey.

KNOCK KNOCK

Knock, knock...
Who's there?
Arthur...
Arthur who?
Arthur any more biscuits in the tin?

Knock, knock...
Who's there?
Ray...
Ray who?
Ray-ning cats and dogs.

Knock, knock...
Who's there?
Arch...
Arch who?
You catching a cold?

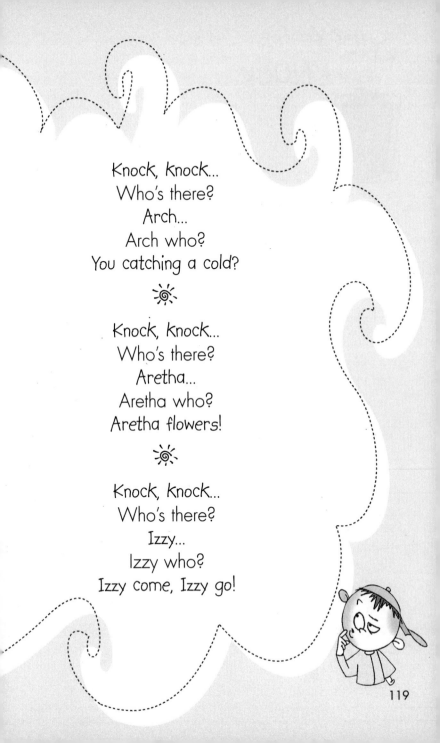

Knock, knock...
Who's there?
Aretha...
Aretha who?
Aretha flowers!

Knock, knock...
Who's there?
Izzy...
Izzy who?
Izzy come, Izzy go!

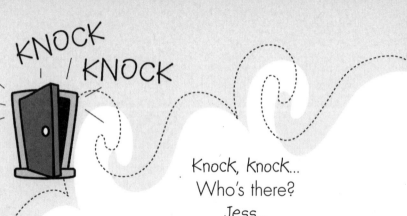

KNOCK KNOCK

Knock, knock...
Who's there?
Jess...
Jess who?
I give up, who?

Knock, knock...
Who's there?
Ben...
Ben who?
Ben knocking on this door all morning!

Knock, knock...
Who's there?
Belize...
Belize who?
Belize in yourself!

Knock, knock...
Who's there?
Brigham...
Brigham who?
Brigham back my sunshine
to me...!

Knock, knock...
Who's there?
Lee King...
Lee King who?
Lee King bucket.

KNOCK
KNOCK

Knock, knock...
Who's there?
Yachts...
Yachts who?
Yachts up, doc?!?

Knock, knock...
Who's there?
Berlin...
Berlin who?
Berlin the water for my
hard boiled eggs!

Knock, knock...
Who's there?
Bera...
Bera who?
Bera necessity!

Knock, knock...
Who's there?
Amana...
Amana who?
Amana *bad* mood!

Knock, knock...
Who's there?
Ginger...
Ginger who?
Ginger hear the doorbell?

KNOCK
KNOCK

Knock, knock...
Who's there?
Bertha...
Bertha who?
Bertha-day greetings!

Knock, knock...
Who's there?
Omar...
Omar who?
Omar goodness gracious,
wrong door!

Knock, knock...
Who's there?
Betty...
Betty who?
Betty ya don't know who this is!

Knock, knock...
Who's there?
Zubin...
Zubin who?
Zubin eating garlic again?

Knock, knock...
Who's there?
Beryl...
Beryl who?
Beryl of beer!

KNOCK KNOCK

Knock, knock...
Who's there?
Don Juan...
Don Juan who?
Don Juan to go to school today?

Knock, knock...
Who's there?
Doughnut...
Doughnut who?
Doughnut open until Christmas!

Knock, knock...
Who's there?
Bjorn...
Bjorn who?
Bjorn Free!

Knock, knock...
Who's there?
Lion...
Lion who?
Lion down on the job again!

Knock, knock...
Who's there?
Bolton...
Bolton who?
Bolton the door!

Knock, knock...
Who's there?
Bjorn...
Bjorn who?
Bjorn with a silver spoon in his mouth!

Knock, knock...
Who's there?
Brad...
Brad who?
Brad news, I'm afraid – this is
the last knock, knock joke!